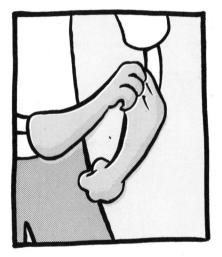

LADY

and the Cyborg Substitute

SCHOLASTIC INC.
New York Toronto London Auckland
Sydney Mexico City New Delhi Hong Kong

Coach Birkby has the kids running laps.

Mr. Johnson is reciting poetry.

Secretary Louanne is looking for her teeth . . . AGAIN!

Ms. Hatford, the music teacher, is flirting in the teachers' lounge.

Mrs. Doris is showing slides of ancient Egypt.

Principal Hernandez is on the phone with parents.

Assistant Principal Stewart is patrolling the halls.

Mrs. Palonski is collaging.

Mr. Edison is mixing chemicals.

BRRII••••○••••NGG

BRRII......NGG!

Later that day . . .

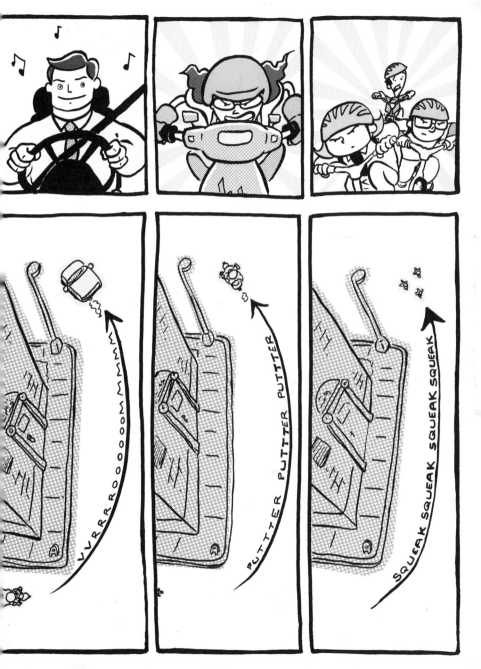

UMPHH!